NURTURE YOUR NESS

CREATIVENESS FORGIVENESS MIND

YFULNESS MINDFULNESS WELLNES

LIGHTHEARTEDNESS MINDFULNESS

NDFULNESS SUCCESSFULNESS OPE

MINDFULNESS HEALTHINESS OPEN

OPEFULNESS DREAMINESS FABULO

ELFISHNESS GENEROUSNESS MIND

CLEARHEADEDNESS MINDFULNESS

MINDFULNESS EAGERNESS FARSIG

EARLESSNESS HOTNESS GRACIOUSN

AWARENESS SPIRITUALNESS CONTE

ORGIVENESS MINDFULNESS CALMN

MINDFULNESS WELLNESS BOOKISH

THRIFTINESS QUIRKINESS ADULTN

NESS OPEN HEARTEDNESS THOUG

NURTURE YOUR NESS

BY BEN MARGHERITA

FIREPLACE PUBLISHING

PURGE THE

NASTINESS

CONTENTS

FINDING NESS

HAPPINESS—THE HOLY GRAIL OF ALL "NESSES"—CAN BE ELUSIVE AT TIMES (LIKE THIS GUY), BUT MINDFULNESS CAN HELP GUIDE YOU TO HAPPINESS' HIDING PLACES. WITH SOME PRACTICE, YOU'LL FIND IT EVERYWHERE YOU LOOK!

By now you've heard of all the benefits of mindfulness. Studies have shown it can reduce stress, combat depression and anxiety, keep you focused, and perhaps most importantly, improve your overall health and well-being. But, for many of us the practice of it seems a bit nebulous. When we think of being mindful, we envision a yogi sitting in a lotus pose with arms extended , eyes closed, "om-ing" away. How can the rest of us be mindful during our day without having to sit quietly on a mountaintop?

In this journal, we set out to guide you on your way to practicing mindfulness with practical (and fun) exercises that you can incorporate into your day-to-day life. And, with a stroll through the dictionary, we will walk through all the "nesses" to guide you on the road to the ultimate goal of a happy and fulfilled life.

Be sure to use this journal each day–not only by working on each week's challenge, but also by reflecting on the activities you've completed and recording your mood. The actual practice of journaling is mindfulness in and of itself. So on day one, you are already starting on your journey to a successful (and happy) future!

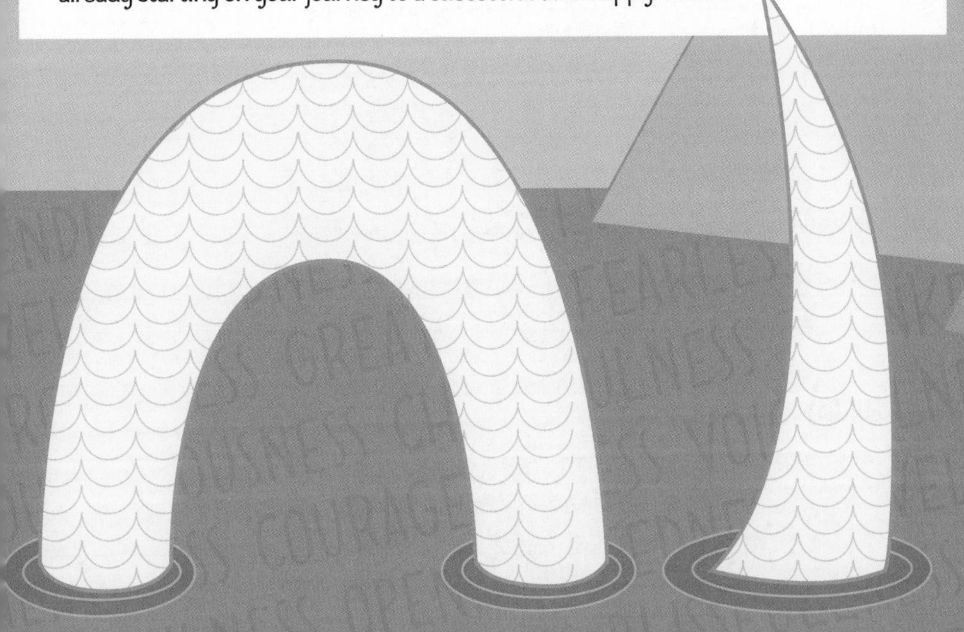

MOOD

Week 1 Date

MONDAY

TUESDAY

WEDNESDAY

THURSDAY

FRIDAY

SATURDAY

SUNDAY

MINDFULNESS

WHAT ARE YOUR STRENGTHS? LIST ALL THE THINGS AT EXCEL AT AND HOW THEY HAVE HELPED YOU ALONG YOUR JOURNEY. ALSO, WRITE SOME OF YOUR WEAKNESSES AND HOW YOU CAN IMPROVE THOSE AREAS.

MOOD

Week 2 Date

MONDAY

=(=(=| =) =)

TUESDAY

=(=(=| =) =)

WEDNESDAY

=(=(=| =) =)

THURSDAY

=(=(=| =) =)

FRIDAY

=(=(=| =) =)

SATURDAY

=(=(=| =) =)

SUNDAY

=(=(=| =) =)

"Think left and think right and think low and think high. Oh, the thinks you can think up if only you try"

DR SEUSS

CREATIVENESS

FILL THIS PAGE WITH IDEAS, DREAMS, AND DOODLES.

MOOD

Week 3 Date

MONDAY

TUESDAY

WEDNESDAY

THURSDAY

FRIDAY

SATURDAY

SUNDAY

"Forgiveness is the fragrance the violet sheds on the heel that has crushed it."

UNKNOWN

FORGIVENESS

WRITE A LETTER OF FORGIVENESS TO SOMEONE WHO HURT YOU. WHAT HAVE YOU DONE TO HEAL?

LET IT GO

A BAD HABIT? HURT FEELINGS? LIST THE THINGS YOU'D LIKE TO LET GO OF THIS YEAR

SLEEPINESS

TRACK YOUR ZZZ'S

HOURS	M	T	W	T	F	S	S
1							
2							
3							
4							
5							
6							
7							
8+							

Week 4 Date

MOOD

MONDAY

TUESDAY

WEDNESDAY

THURSDAY

FRIDAY

SATURDAY

SUNDAY

MINDFULNESS

DESCRIBE THE PERFECT DAY. WHERE WOULD YOU BE? WHO WOULD BE WITH YOU? WHAT WOULD YOU DO? HOW CAN YOU WORK TOWARD MAKING EACH DAY PERFECT?

Week 5 Date

MOOD

MONDAY

TUESDAY

WEDNESDAY

THURSDAY

FRIDAY

SATURDAY

SUNDAY

"Every time you are tempted to react in the same old way, ask if you want to be a prisoner of the past or a pioneer of the future."

DEEPAK CHOPRA

CALMNESS

WHILE YOU ARE COLORING THIS MANDALA, TRY TO CLEAR YOUR MIND AND FOCUS ON YOUR BREATHING.

COLOR YOURSELF CALM, SEE PAGE 130

JUST DO IT (AGAIN & AGAIN)

WHAT RITUALS COULD YOU ADD TO YOUR DAY, WEEK OR MONTH?

RUN • YOGA • TAP • CROCHET • SING • JUICE • PRAY • MEDITATE • STRETCH

ART • TEA • COOK • STARGAZE • AFFIRMATIONS • GARDEN • STRETCH • NAP

KNIT • TAI CHI • CLEAN • WRITE • BIRD-WATCH • DANCE • DAYDREAM • BLOG

BAKE • WALK • EXPLORE • JOURNAL • READ • HANDWRITE LETTERS • FAST

MOOD

Week 6 Date

MONDAY

TUESDAY

WEDNESDAY

THURSDAY

FRIDAY

SATURDAY

SUNDAY

"There's not a word yet for old friends who've just met."

JIM HENSON

CHUMMINESS

MAKE AN EFFORT TO BE FRIENDLY TO AT LEAST FOUR PEOPLE THIS WEEK.
WRITE ABOUT THE EXPERIENCES. DOODLE THEIR FACES IN THE CIRCLES BELOW.

GOOD HUMOR

DRAW A COMIC STRIP OF SOMETHING FUNNY THAT HAPPENED THIS WEEK.

Week 7 Date

MOOD

MONDAY

TUESDAY

WEDNESDAY

THURSDAY

FRIDAY

SATURDAY

SUNDAY

"We cannot cure the world of sorrows, but we can choose to live in joy."

JOSEPH CAMPBELL

JOYFULNESS

DRAW A PICTURE OF YOUR HAPPY PLACE OR YOUR HAPPIEST MEMORY.
TAKE TIME TO REMEMBER ALL THE DETAILS.

Week 8 Date

MOOD

MONDAY

=(=(=| =) =)

TUESDAY

=(=(=| =) =)

WEDNESDAY

=(=(=| =) =)

THURSDAY

=(=(=| =) =)

FRIDAY

=(=(=| =) =)

SATURDAY

=(=(=| =) =)

SUNDAY

=(=(=| =) =)

MINDFULNESS

REFLECT ON THE GOOD HEALTH YOU'VE ENJOYED IN YOUR LIFE. HOW CAN YOU MAINTAIN AND EVEN IMPROVE YOUR GOOD HEALTH?

Week 9 Date

MOOD

MONDAY

TUESDAY

WEDNESDAY

THURSDAY

FRIDAY

SATURDAY

SUNDAY

"Money cannot buy health, but I'd settle for a diamond-studded wheelchair."

DOROTHY PARKER

WELLNESS

HEALTHIER EATING? WORKOUT CLASS? 5K TRAINING?
START A WELLNESS PROGRAM AND KEEP TRACK OF YOUR RESULTS.

	MONDAY	TUESDAY	WEDNESDAY	THURSDAY	FRIDAY	SATURDAY	SUNDAY
MEDITATE							
HIKE							
RUN							
GYM							
JUICE							
WEIGHT TRAIN							
YOGA							
FITNESS CLASS							
WALK							
PUSH-UPS							
SIT-UPS							
SPIN CLASS							
FASTING							
HEALTHY EATING							
MASSAGE							
PILATES							

Week 10 Date

MOOD

MONDAY

TUESDAY

WEDNESDAY

THURSDAY

FRIDAY

SATURDAY

SUNDAY

"You can never get a cup of tea large enough or a book long enough to suit me."

C.S. LEWIS

BOOKISHNESS

WRITE THE NAMES OF SOME BOOKS YOU PLAN ON READING IN THE NEAR FUTURE.

Week 11 Date

MOOD

MONDAY

TUESDAY

WEDNESDAY

THURSDAY

FRIDAY

SATURDAY

SUNDAY

"A light heart lives long."

WILLIAM SHAKESPEARE

LIGHTHEARTEDNESS

DRAW A COMIC STRIP OF THE FUNNIEST THING THAT EVER HAPPENED TO YOU.

Week 12 Date

MOOD

MONDAY

=(=(=| =) =)

TUESDAY

=(=(=| =) =)

WEDNESDAY

=(=(=| =) =)

THURSDAY

=(=(=| =) =)

FRIDAY

=(=(=| =) =)

SATURDAY

=(=(=| =) =)

SUNDAY

=(=(=| =) =)

MINDFULNESS

REFLECT ON THE PEOPLE IN YOUR LIFE WHO HAVE HELPED YOU ALONG YOUR JOURNEY. FAMILY, FRIENDS, TEACHERS, NEIGHBORS. HOW HAVE THEY HELPED YOU TO BECOME THE PERSON YOU ARE TODAY?

Week 13 Date

MOOD

MONDAY

TUESDAY

WEDNESDAY

THURSDAY

FRIDAY

SATURDAY

SUNDAY

"It is thrifty to prepare today for the wants of tomorrow."

AESOP

THRIFTINESS

DREAMING OF A NEW PAIR OF SHOES OR A TRIP TO EUROPE?
STAY ON TRACK BY KEEPING TRACK OF YOUR SAVINGS.

$ ______ $ ______ $ ______ $ ______ $ ______

$ ______ $ ______ $ ______ $ ______

$ ______ $ ______ $ ______

I'M SAVING FOR ______ $ ______ $ ______ MY GOAL DATE IS ______

Goal
$ ______

Week 14 Date

MOOD

MONDAY

TUESDAY

WEDNESDAY

THURSDAY

FRIDAY

SATURDAY

SUNDAY

"It is health that is the real wealth, and not pieces of gold and silver."

MAHATMA GANDHI

HEALTHINESS

WITH SOME EXERCISE, HEALTHY EATING AND REGULAR DOCTOR VISITS, YOU CAN COMPLETELY GAIN CONTROL OF YOUR HEALTH IN 90 DAYS. START A HEALTH CRAZE USING THE CHART BELOW.

1	2	3	4	5	6	7	8	9	10
11	12	13	14	15	16	17	18	19	20
21	22	23	24	25	26	27	28	29	30
31	32	33	34	35	36	37	38	39	40
41	42	43	44	45	46	47	48	49	50
51	52	53	54	55	56	57	58	59	60
61	62	63	64	65	66	67	68	69	70
71	72	73	74	75	76	77	78	79	80
81	82	83	84	85	86	87	88	89	90

TO PLAN YOUR ENTIRE YEAR, SEE PAGE 140

KEY

MAKE A KEY FOR YOUR HEALTH GOALS USING DIFFERENT COLOR DOTS OR SYMBOLS AND RECORD THEM ON THE DAYS YOU ACCOMPLISH THEM.

- ☐ DOCTOR VISIT
- ☐ CARDIO
- ☐ HEALTHY EATING
- ☐ MEDITATION
- ☐ YOGA
- ☐ GOOD SLEEP
- ☐ JUICING
- ☐ STRETCHING
- ☐ SPINNING
- ☐ MASSAGE THERAPY
- ☐ ACUPUNCTURE
- ☐ HYDRATION
- ☐ ___________
- ☐ ___________
- ☐ ___________
- ☐ ___________
- ☐ ___________
- ☐ ___________

Week 15 Date

MOOD

MONDAY

TUESDAY

WEDNESDAY

THURSDAY

FRIDAY

SATURDAY

SUNDAY

"The great challenge of adulthood is holding on to your idealism after you lose your innocence."

BRUCE SPRINGSTEEN

ADULTNESS

WRITE A LETTER TO YOUR YOUNGER SELF. WHAT DIFFICULT SITUATIONS HAVE YOU MANAGED SUCCESSFULLY AS A GROWN-UP? HOW HAVE THINGS CHANGED FOR THE BETTER?

ADULT EDUCATION

BEFORE CALLING YOUR DAD TO FIX A FLAT, WATCH SOME YOUTUBE VIDEOS AND DIY! LIST THE SKILLS YOU'D LIKE TO LEARN BELOW.

Week 16 Date

MOOD

MONDAY

TUESDAY

WEDNESDAY

THURSDAY

FRIDAY

SATURDAY

SUNDAY

MINDFULNESS

WHAT ARE YOU MOST GRATEFUL FOR IN YOUR LIFE? YOUR HOME? YOUR CAREER? YOUR LOVED ONES?

WRITE A THANK-YOU LETTER FOR THE THINGS OR PEOPLE YOU ARE MOST GRATEFUL FOR.

MOOD

Week 17 Date

MONDAY

TUESDAY

WEDNESDAY

THURSDAY

FRIDAY

SATURDAY

SUNDAY

"All progress takes place outside the comfortzone."

MICHAEL JOHN BOBAK

SUCCESSFULNESS

JOT DOWN YOUR GOALS ON LABELS (SEE PAGE 120). CUT THEM OUT AND PLACE IN A BOWL ON YOUR NIGHTSTAND. PULL OUT ONE WHENEVER YOU NEED A NEW CHALLENGE.

MOOD

Week 18 Date

MONDAY

TUESDAY

WEDNESDAY

THURSDAY

FRIDAY

SATURDAY

SUNDAY

"I've learned that whenever I decide something with an open heart, I usually make the right decision."

MAYA ANGELOU

OPEN-HEARTEDNESS

LIVING OPEN-HEARTED MEANS TO LET YOUR GUARD DOWN, SOFTEN YOUR HEART, AND BE EMPATHIC TO OTHERS. HOW CAN YOU BE MORE OPEN-HEARTED? WHO IN YOUR LIFE DESERVES YOUR EMPATHY AND WHY? BE SPECIFIC.

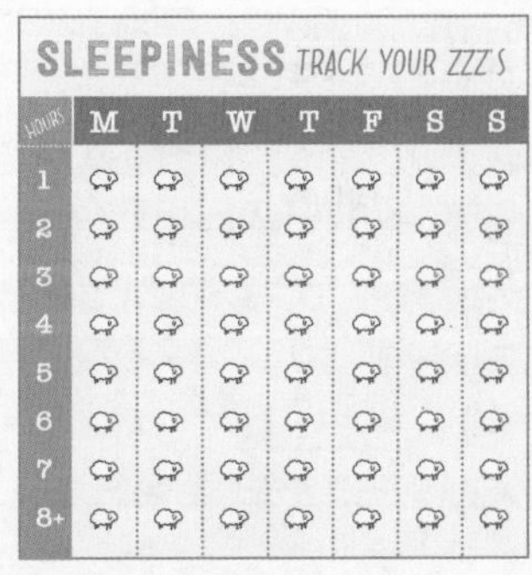

MOOD

Week 19 Date

MONDAY

TUESDAY

WEDNESDAY

THURSDAY

FRIDAY

SATURDAY

SUNDAY

"If there were one word that could act as a standard of conduct for one's entire life, perhaps it would be 'thoughtfulness.'"

CONFUCIUS

THOUGHTFULNESS

DOODLE A MEME IN ONE OF THE BOXES BELOW (OR USE THE ONE PROVIDED), SNAP A PIC WITH YOUR PHONE, AND SEND IT TO SOMEONE TO BRIGHTEN THEIR DAY.

HOPE YOU HAVE A MAGICAL DAY!

FOR MORE MEMES, SEE PAGE 118

MANTRA MANIA

WRITE DOWN YOUR MANTRA FOR THIS WEEK, THIS MONTH, THIS YEAR.

Week 20 Date

MOOD

MONDAY

TUESDAY

WEDNESDAY

THURSDAY

FRIDAY

SATURDAY

SUNDAY

MINDFULNESS

WHAT WOULD MAKE YOUR DAY GREAT? HOW CAN YOU CREATE THE PERFECT DAY?

MOOD

Week 21 Date

MONDAY

=(=(=| =) =)

TUESDAY

=(=(=| =) =)

WEDNESDAY

=(=(=| =) =)

THURSDAY

=(=(=| =) =)

FRIDAY

=(=(=| =) =)

SATURDAY

=(=(=| =) =)

SUNDAY

=(=(=| =) =)

"Accept no one's definition of your life; define yourself."

HARVEY FIERSTEIN

QUIRKINESS

LOVE TO WEAR FUNKY GLASSES? HATE PEAS ON THE SAME PLATE AS YOUR MASHED POTATOES? WRITE A LIST OF ALL THE QUIRKY LIKES AND DISLIKES THAT MAKE YOU, YOU!

SLEEPINESS TRACK YOUR ZZZ'S

HOURS	M	T	W	T	F	S	S
1							
2							
3							
4							
5							
6							
7							
8+							

MOOD

Week 22 Date

MONDAY

TUESDAY

WEDNESDAY

THURSDAY

FRIDAY

SATURDAY

SUNDAY

"Anyone who keeps on learning not only remains young but becomes constantly more valuable."

HENRY FORD

OPEN-MINDEDNESS

WHAT THOUGHTS HAVE YOU HELD ABOUT A PARTICULAR TOPIC THAT YOU COULD TAKE MORE TIME TO UNDERSTAND OR RETHINK? SEEK OUT FRIENDS WITH A DIFFERENT POINT OF VIEW, LISTEN TO WHAT THEY SAY, AND WRITE WHAT YOU'VE LEARNED.

MOOD

Week 23 Date

MONDAY

TUESDAY

WEDNESDAY

THURSDAY

FRIDAY

SATURDAY

SUNDAY

"To be yourself in a world that is constantly trying to make you something else is the greatest accomplishment."

RALPH WALDO EMERSON

COOLNESS

THERE'S A LOT YOU CAN LEARN FROM A COOL CAT. BELOW ARE SOME TRAITS OF THE TRAGICALLY HIP. RATE YOURSELF BY SHADING-IN SOME SHADES IN EACH CATEGORY AND SEE WHERE YOU CAN IMPROVE.

	1	2	3	4	5	6	7	8	9	10
CONFIDENT										
KIND										
GOOD LISTENER										
CHILL										
ALWAYS LEARNING										
POSITIVE ATTITUDE										
CREATIVE										
CARE IN APPEARANCE										
EXERCISES										
OUTSPOKEN										
ENJOYS MUSIC										
INDEPENDENT										
NON-REACTIONARY										

THIS WEEK'S WIN

MOOD

Week 24 Date

MONDAY

TUESDAY

WEDNESDAY

THURSDAY

FRIDAY

SATURDAY

SUNDAY

MINDFULNESS

SPEND SOME TIME IN NATURE. BE PRESENT, NOTICE THE LEAVES, NOTICE THE SKY AND YOUR SURROUNDINGS. TRY TO IDENTIFY DIFFERENT BIRDS AND TREES. REFLECT ON HOW YOU FEEL WHEN YOU ARE IN NATURE. WRITE ABOUT YOUR EXPERIENCE.

Week 25 Date

MOOD

MONDAY

TUESDAY

WEDNESDAY

THURSDAY

FRIDAY

SATURDAY

SUNDAY

"May your choices reflect your hopes, not your fears."

NELSON MANDELA

HOPEFULNESS

IMAGINE THESE PRESENTS CONTAINED THE THINGS YOU'VE ALWAYS DREAMED OF...WHAT WOULD BE INSIDE? THINK BEYOND MATERIAL THINGS.

MOOD

Week 26 Date

MONDAY

TUESDAY

WEDNESDAY

THURSDAY

FRIDAY

SATURDAY

SUNDAY

"The biggest adventure you can take is to live the life of your dreams."

OPRAH WINFREY

DREAMINESS

ALLOW YOURSELF TIME TO DAYDREAM. TUNE OUT ALL THE DISTRACTIONS AND TRY TO ENTER A STATE OF TOTAL RELAXATION. LET YOUR MIND WANDER. RECORD YOUR EXPERIENCE..

SLEEPINESS *TRACK YOUR ZZZ'S*

HOURS	M	T	W	T	F	S	S
1							
2							
3							
4							
5							
6							
7							
8+							

Week 27 Date

MOOD

MONDAY

TUESDAY

WEDNESDAY

THURSDAY

FRIDAY

SATURDAY

SUNDAY

"The most important thing is to live a fabulous life. As long as it's fabulous, I don't care how long it is."

FREDDIE MERCURY

FABULOUSNESS

IF YOU WANT TO BE FABULOUS, YOU GOTTA WERRRK!

TAKE A LUXURIOUS BATH

KISS ON BOTH CHEEKS

PICK UP THE TAB

MASTER THE PERFECT COSMO

BINGE-WATCH, *ABSOLUTELY FABULOUS*

BE KIND TO STRANGERS

TIP LIKE A BALLER

HAVE A KITCHEN DANCE PARTY

USE THE WORD "DAHHLING!"

WEAR SOMETHING SPARKLY

LEARN SOME FRENCH

LIP-SYNCH TO, "AND I AM TELLING YOU I'M NOT GOING"

SELFIE, SELFIE, SELFIE!

SEND YOURSELF FLOWERS

BINGE-WATCH, *RUPAUL'S DRAG RACE*

KARAOKE, BUT MAKE IT FASHION

MANI, PEDI, REPEAT

PAMPER YOUR POOCH

TRY A NEW BEAUTY ROUTINE

HIRE A GLAM SQUAD

USE CLOTH NAPKINS WITH TAKEOUT

MOOD

Week 28 Date

MONDAY

TUESDAY

WEDNESDAY

THURSDAY

FRIDAY

SATURDAY

SUNDAY

MINDFULNESS

REFLECT ON A NEGATIVE EXPERIENCE YOU HAD IN YOUR LIFE. HOW DID IT AFFECT YOU? WHAT TOOLS DO YOU HAVE TODAY THAT WOULD PREVENT THAT RESULT FROM HAPPENING IN THE FUTURE?

MOOD

Week 29 Date

MONDAY

TUESDAY

WEDNESDAY

THURSDAY

FRIDAY

SATURDAY

SUNDAY

"When all else fails, cleaning house is the perfect antidote to most of life's ills."

SUE GRAFTON

CLEANLINESS

NEXT TO GODLINESS (ANOTHER "NESS"!), CLEANLINESS CAN BRING YOU PEACE. SO DON YOUR RUBBER GLOVES, CRANK UP SOME ARETHA, AND GET BUSY!!

	MONDAY	TUESDAY	WEDNESDAY	THURSDAY	FRIDAY	SATURDAY	SUNDAY
DE-CLUTTER							
SWEEP							
MOP							
VACUUM							
LAUNDRY							
MAKE BEDS							
DUST							
CLEAN TOILET							
SCRUB TUB							
ORGANIZE							
PURGE							
TAKE OUT TRASH							
TOWELS/SHEETS							
CLEAN OUT FRIDGE							
UNLOAD DISHWASHER							

MOOD

Week 30 Date

MONDAY

TUESDAY

WEDNESDAY

THURSDAY

FRIDAY

SATURDAY

SUNDAY

"Daring to set boundaries is about having the courage to love ourselves, even when we risk disappointing others."

BRENÉ BROWN

SELFISHNESS

BEING SELFISH CAN BE A POSITIVE, PARTICULARLY IF YOU SPEND ALL YOUR TIME AND ENERGY ON OTHERS' NEEDS. DO YOU THINK PEOPLE TAKE ADVANTAGE OF YOUR KINDNESS? WRITE ABOUT A SITUATION THAT MADE YOU FEEL THAT WAY. ASK YOURSELF HOW YOU CAN SET BOUNDARIES.

NESS HUNTING

NOW THAT YOU'VE BEEN PRACTICING AWHILE, WHICH NESS HAS BEEN THE MOST ELUSIVE IN YOUR LIFE?

MOOD

Week 31 Date

MONDAY

TUESDAY

WEDNESDAY

THURSDAY

FRIDAY

SATURDAY

SUNDAY

"Never worry about numbers. Help one person at a time and always start with the person nearest you."

MOTHER TERESA

GENEROUSNESS

BEING GENEROUS CAN BE AS EASY AS LEAVING AN EXTRA BIG TIP.
CHECK OFF AS MANY ACTS OF GENEROUSNESS AS YOU CAN!

- [ ] OFFER TO HELP SOMEONE IN NEED
- [ ] MAKE A DONATION TO CHARITY
- [ ] HELP AN ELDERLY PERSON
- [ ] CALL A FRIEND WHO IS DOWN
- [ ] DONATE YOUR TIME TO A CAUSE
- [ ] PAY IT FORWARD
- [ ] GIVE SOMEONE A COMPLIMENT
- [ ] INVITE A CO-WORKER TO DINNER

- [ ] SMILE
- [ ] PURGE YOUR CLOSET AND DONATE
- [ ] RECOMMEND SOMEONE FOR A JOB
- [ ] RAISE AWARENESS FOR A CAUSE
- [ ] VOLUNTEER
- [ ] BEFRIEND SOMEONE LONELY
- [ ] BAKE A TREAT FOR A CAKE SALE
- [ ] SEND A CARD TO A SICK RELATIVE

- [ ] BE COMPASSIONATE
- [ ] LISTEN MORE
- [ ] HOLD THE DOOR OPEN
- [ ] OFFER TO HELP A NEIGHBOR
- [ ] BUY SOMEONE A COFFEE
- [ ] SEND FLOWERS TO A FRIEND
- [ ] CHEER ON AN ATHLETE
- [ ] PUT CHANGE IN AN EXPIRED METER

Week 32 Date

MOOD

MONDAY

TUESDAY

WEDNESDAY

THURSDAY

FRIDAY

SATURDAY

SUNDAY

MINDFULNESS

WHAT ARE THE ACTIVITIES YOU MOST ENJOY DOING? HOW CAN YOU FIND MORE TIME TO ENGAGE IN THINGS YOU ENJOY? HOW CAN YOU BRING MORE JOY TO THE TASKS YOU DREAD?

MOOD

Week 33 Date

MONDAY

TUESDAY

WEDNESDAY

THURSDAY

FRIDAY

SATURDAY

SUNDAY

"I do not live to play, but I play in order that I may live, and return with greater zest to the labors of life."

PLATO

ZESTFULNESS

BEING MINDFUL OF HOW YOU USE YOUR TIME WILL HELP YOU TAKE THE BIGGEST BITE OUT OF LIFE. CHECK OFF AS MANY ACTIVITIES AS YOU CAN.

- [ ] TAKE A ROAD TRIP
- [ ] SKYDIVE
- [ ] KISS A LOVER
- [ ] SPEND TIME IN NATURE
- [ ] TRY NEW FOODS
- [ ] SEE A SHOW
- [ ] SING IN THE RAIN
- [ ] TRAVEL
- [ ] LEARN A LANGUAGE
- [ ] DANCE, DANCE, DANCE
- [ ] TALK TO STRANGERS
- [ ] BE OPTIMISTIC
- [ ] PLAY A SPORT
- [ ] TAKE LONG WALKS
- [ ] PLAN A BEACH DAY
- [ ] AVOID NEGATIVITY
- [ ] ENJOY THE MOMENT
- [ ] WINE TASTE
- [ ] CREATE
- [ ] READ POETRY
- [ ] WEAR BRIGHT COLORS
- [ ] SOCIALIZE
- [ ] CALL AN OLD FLAME
- [ ] BUNGEE JUMP

MOOD

Week 34 Date

MONDAY

=(=(=| =) =)

TUESDAY

=(=(=| =) =)

WEDNESDAY

=(=(=| =) =)

THURSDAY

=(=(=| =) =)

FRIDAY

=(=(=| =) =)

SATURDAY

=(=(=| =) =)

SUNDAY

=(=(=| =) =)

"The simplest man with passion will be more persuasive than the most eloquent without."

FRANCOIS DE LA ROCHEFOUCAULD

PERSUASIVENESS

CONFIDENCE AIDS PERSUASIVENESS. THIS WEEK TRY TO PERSUADE SOMEONE TO DO SOMETHING. IT COULD BE AS SIMPLE AS GETTING A COUCH POTATO TO TAKE A WALK WITH YOU. BE AWARE OF YOUR BODY LANGUAGE WHILE YOU'RE MAKING YOUR CASE, LISTEN INTENTLY AND SPEAK CLEARLY. WRITE ABOUT YOUR SUCCESS OR FAILURE BELOW.

Week 35 Date

MOOD

MONDAY

TUESDAY

WEDNESDAY

THURSDAY

FRIDAY

SATURDAY

SUNDAY

"Remember; no matter how desperate the situation seems, time spent thinking clearly is never time wasted."

MAX BROOKS

CLEARHEADEDNESS

WHILE YOU ARE COLORING THIS MANDALA, TRY TO CLEAR YOUR MIND AND FOCUS ON YOUR BREATHING.

COLOR YOURSELF CALM, SEE PAGE 130

NESS TRACKER

NOW THAT YOU'VE BEEN PRACTICING FOR AWHILE, JOT DOWN THREE "NESSES" YOU'VE BEEN WORKING ON AND RATE YOUR PROGRESS.

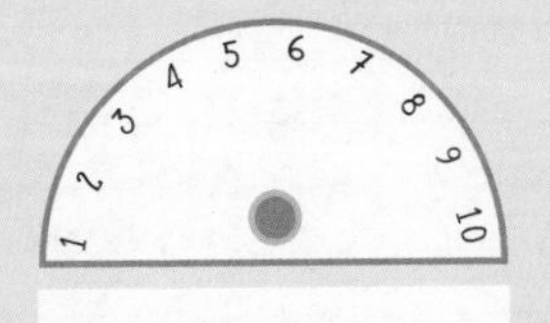

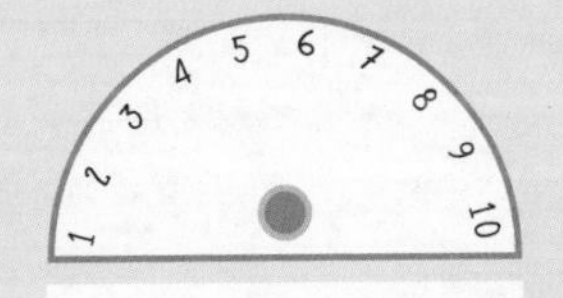

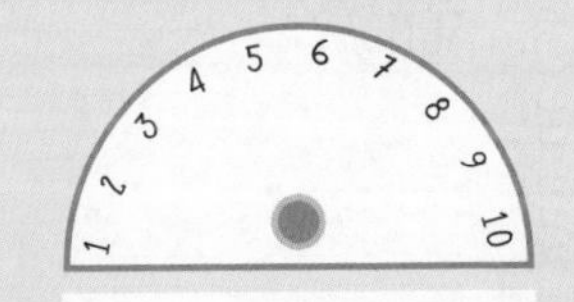

MOOD

Week 36 Date

MONDAY

TUESDAY

WEDNESDAY

THURSDAY

FRIDAY

SATURDAY

SUNDAY

MINDFULNESS

WHAT ARE THE BIGGEST SUCCESSES IN YOUR LIFE? HOW CAN YOU HAVE MORE OF THEM? CONVERSELY, WHAT IS YOUR BIGGEST FAILURE?

MOOD

Week 37 Date

MONDAY

TUESDAY

WEDNESDAY

THURSDAY

FRIDAY

SATURDAY

SUNDAY

"Reflect upon your present blessings of which every man has many—not on your past misfortunes, of which all men have some."

CHARLES DICKENS

GRATEFULNESS

FILL THIS PAGE WITH EVERYTHING YOU ARE GRATEFUL FOR.

COLOR YOURSELF CALM, SEE PAGE 130

Week 38 Date

MOOD

MONDAY

TUESDAY

WEDNESDAY

THURSDAY

FRIDAY

SATURDAY

SUNDAY

"Be nice to nerds. Chances are you'll end up working for one."

BILL GATES

NERDINESS

WRITE IN THE NAMES OF SOME NON-FICTION BOOKS YOU PLAN ON READING IN THE NEAR FUTURE. BE SURE TO INCLUDE A MIX OF TOPICS.

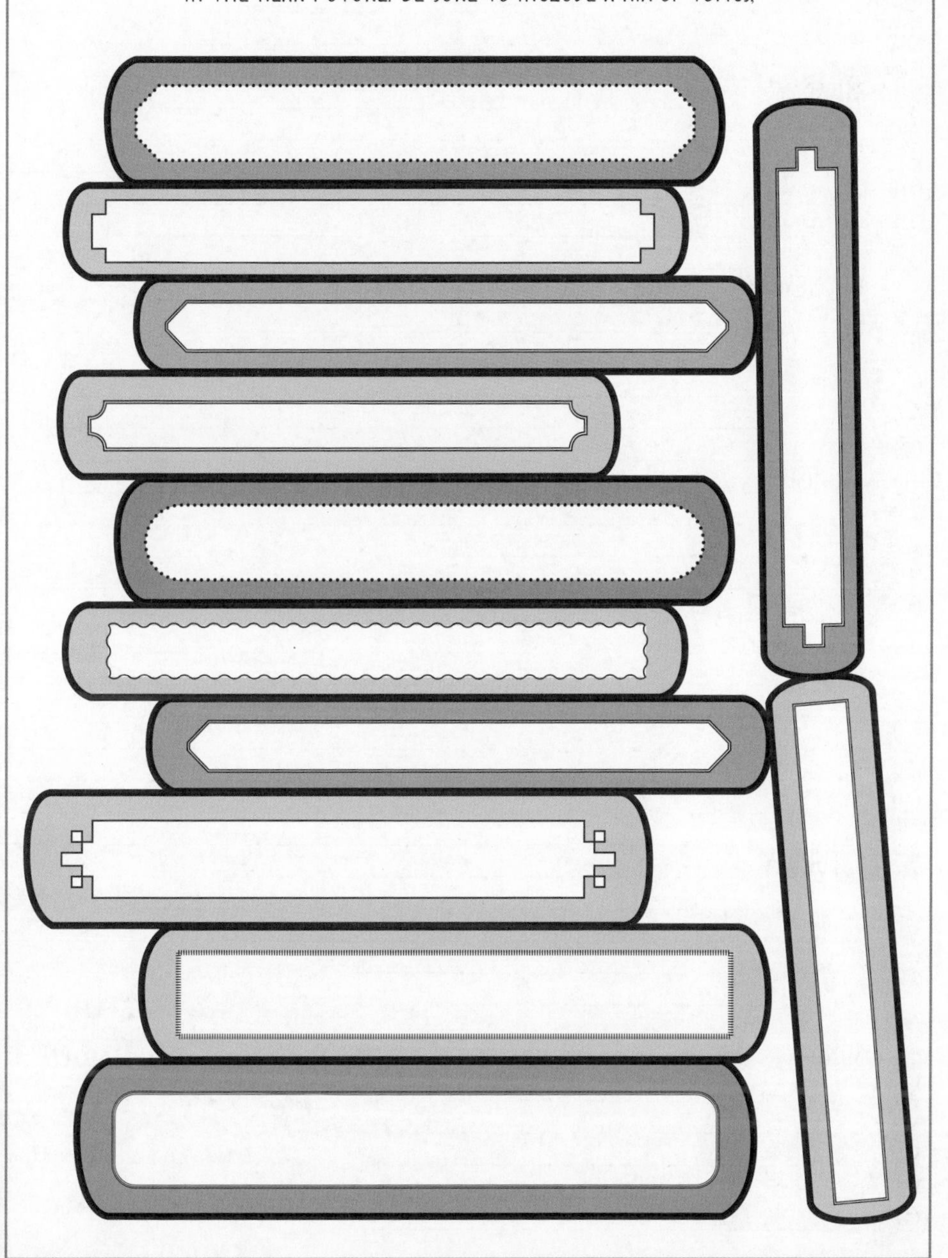

MOOD

Week 39 Date

MONDAY

TUESDAY

WEDNESDAY

THURSDAY

FRIDAY

SATURDAY

SUNDAY

"All that an obstacle does with brave men is, not to frighten them, but to challenge them."

WOODROW WILSON

BRAVENESS

YOU DON'T HAVE TO JUMP OUT OF A PLANE OR BUNGEE JUMP FROM A BRIDGE TO BE BRAVE. SOMETIMES BEING BRAVE CAN BE ASKING SOMEONE FOR HELP OR BEING VULNERABLE. TRY DOING SOMETHING BRAVE, EITHER PHYSICALLY OR EMOTIONALLY, AND WRITE ABOUT YOUR EXPERIENCE.

THIS WEEK'S WIN

Week 40 Date

MOOD

MONDAY

TUESDAY

WEDNESDAY

THURSDAY

FRIDAY

SATURDAY

SUNDAY

MINDFULNESS

WHAT DO YOU PROCRASTINATE THE MOST ABOUT? WHAT FEELINGS DO YOU HAVE ABOUT THAT TASK WHILE YOU ARE DOING IT? WHEN YOU'VE COMPLETED IT? WHAT WOULD MAKE IT EASIER/BETTER?

Week 47 Date

MOOD

MONDAY

TUESDAY

WEDNESDAY

THURSDAY

FRIDAY

SATURDAY

SUNDAY

"If a man is gracious and courteous to strangers, it shows he is a citizen of the world."

FRANCIS BACON

GRACIOUSNESS

HOST A DINNER PARTY WITH FRIENDS. INVITE AT LEAST ONE PERSON YOU DON'T KNOW REALLY WELL. GO THE EXTRA MILE TO MAKE EVERY GUEST FEEL WELCOME. WRITE ABOUT THE EVENT BELOW.

THANK YOU

WRITE A THANK-YOU NOTE TO SOMEONE, EITHER LIVING OR DEAD, WHO DID SOMETHING MEANINGFUL FOR YOU.

Week 42 Date

MOOD

MONDAY

TUESDAY

WEDNESDAY

THURSDAY

FRIDAY

SATURDAY

SUNDAY

"The most reliable way to predict the future is to create it."

ABRAHAM LINCOLN

FARSIGHTEDNESS

CREATE A VISION BOARD BY CUTTING AND PASTING IMAGES THAT REPRESENT YOUR FUTURE GOALS. BE SURE TO REFLECT ON IT OFTEN.

Week 43 Date

MOOD

MONDAY

TUESDAY

WEDNESDAY

THURSDAY

FRIDAY

SATURDAY

SUNDAY

"To make the world a friendly place, one must show it a friendly face."

JAMES WHITCOMB RILEY

FRIENDLINESS

ADDING TO YOUR SOCIAL CIRCLE IS ALWAYS A GOOD IDEA. WHO WOULD YOU LIKE TO BRING IN TO THE LOOP AND WHY? WHO IS ALREADY IN YOUR LOOP THAT YOU'D LIKE TO BE CLOSER TO?

Week 44 Date

MOOD

MONDAY

TUESDAY

WEDNESDAY

THURSDAY

FRIDAY

SATURDAY

SUNDAY

MINDFULNESS

HOW HAS PRACTICING MINDFULNESS ENRICHED YOUR LIFE? WRITE ABOUT A SPECIFIC INSTANCE BELOW.

MOOD

Week 45 Date

MONDAY

TUESDAY

WEDNESDAY

THURSDAY

FRIDAY

SATURDAY

SUNDAY

"Everything you want is on the other side of fear."

JACK CANFIELD

FEARLESSNESS

THIS WEEK, DO SOMETHING THAT SCARES YOU. WRITE ABOUT THE EXPERIENCE BELOW. DID YOU OVERCOME YOUR FEAR? WILL YOU DO IT AGAIN?

THIS WEEK'S WIN

MOOD

Week 46 Date

MONDAY

TUESDAY

WEDNESDAY

THURSDAY

FRIDAY

SATURDAY

SUNDAY

"One of the most attractive things about the flowers is their beautiful reserve."

HENRY DAVID THOREAU

HOTNESS

OK, SO WE ALL MIGHT NOT BE SUPERMODELS, BUT THERE ARE PLENTY OF WAYS TO UP YOUR HOTNESS. RATE YOURSELF AND SEE WHAT NEEDS WORK.

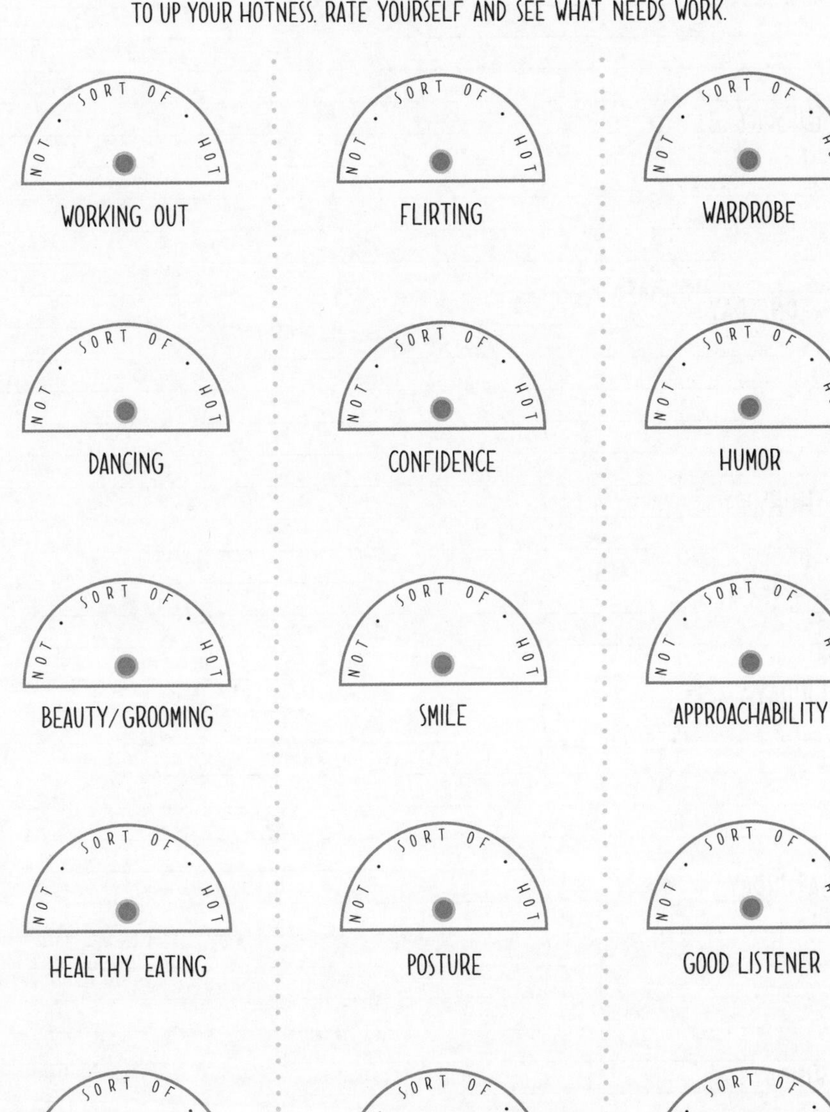

Week 41 Date

MOOD

MONDAY

TUESDAY

WEDNESDAY

THURSDAY

FRIDAY

SATURDAY

SUNDAY

"The secret of getting ahead is getting started."

MARK TWAIN

EAGERNESS

BEING EAGER TO HELP OTHERS IS ONE THING, BUT WHAT ABOUT BEING EAGER TO CREATE SUCCESS IN YOUR LIFE? TRY SOME OF THESE IDEAS TO HELP YOU CONQUER THE DAY!

- [ ] PLAN YOUR DAY THE NIGHT BEFORE
- [ ] GET A GOOD NIGHT'S SLEEP
- [ ] WAKE UP EARLY
- [ ] STRETCH
- [ ] MAKE YOUR BED
- [ ] MEDITATE
- [ ] VISUALIZE YOUR SUCCESS
- [ ] CHECK YOUR TO-DO LIST
- [ ] DON'T THINK-JUST DO
- [ ] REPEAT YOUR MANTRA
- [ ] TUNE OUT DISTRACTIONS
- [ ] STICK TO A ROUTINE
- [ ] WRITE TOMORROW'S TO-DO LIST
- [ ] PLAN, PLAN, PLAN
- [ ] CELEBRATE EVERY WIN

SEE IT, BE IT

MAKE A MINI VISION BOARD. CUT AND PASTE IMAGES THAT REPRESENT THE GOALS YOU WOULD LIKE TO ACHIEVE IN YOUR LIFE.

Week 48 Date

MOOD

MONDAY

TUESDAY

WEDNESDAY

THURSDAY

FRIDAY

SATURDAY

SUNDAY

MINDFULNESS

LIST SOME QUALITIES OF OTHER PEOPLE IN YOUR LIFE THAT YOU ADMIRE. HAVE YOU EVER COMPLIMENTED THEM ON THESE QUALITIES? HOW CAN YOU LEARN FROM THEM?

MOOD

Week 49 Date

MONDAY

TUESDAY

WEDNESDAY

THURSDAY

FRIDAY

SATURDAY

SUNDAY

"Be loving, and you will be lovable. Be open and receptive to love."

LOUISE HAY

RECEPTIVENESS

BEING RECEPTIVE CAN OPEN YOUR MIND AS WELL AS YOUR HEART.
IT REQUIRES YOU TO DROP YOUR DEFENSES, BE OPEN, BE CURIOUS, AND TO LISTEN.
THIS WEEK, TRY TO BE RECEPTIVE TO SOMEONE ELSE'S OPINIONS, THOUGHTS–
OR EVEN COMPLIMENTS! WRITE ABOUT YOUR EXPERIENCES BELOW.

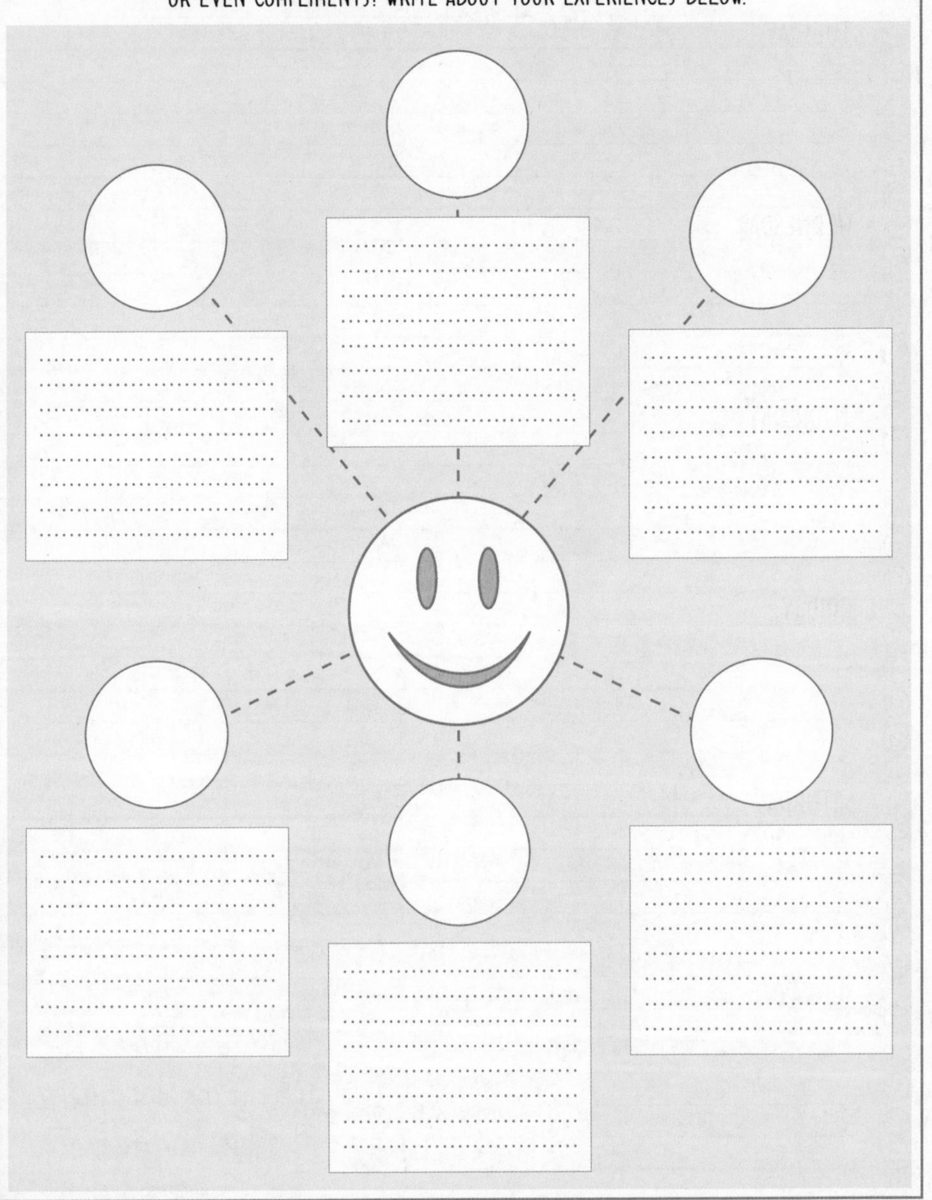

MOOD

Week 50 Date

MONDAY

TUESDAY

WEDNESDAY

THURSDAY

FRIDAY

SATURDAY

SUNDAY

"Awareness is the greatest agent for change."

ECKHART TOLLE

AWARENESS

BEING SELF-AWARE CAN HELP YOU TO IMPROVE ON WEAKNESSES AND IMPROVE ON STRENGTHS. LIST SOME OF YOUR STRENGTHS AND WEAKNESSES BELOW. REFLECT ON EACH. ALSO, ASK A TRUSTED FRIEND TO DESCRIBE SOME OF YOUR STRENGTHS AND WEAKNESSES, COMPARE THE LISTS AND REFLECT ON THEM.

MOOD

Week 51 Date

MONDAY

TUESDAY

WEDNESDAY

THURSDAY

FRIDAY

SATURDAY

SUNDAY

"Faith is to believe what you do not see; the reward of this faith is to see what you believe."

SAINT AUGUSTINE

SPIRITUALNESS

REFLECT ON YOUR SPIRITUALITY. WHAT DOES BEING SPIRITUAL MEAN IN YOUR LIFE?

SLEEPINESS *TRACK YOUR ZZZ'S*

HOURS	M	T	W	T	F	S	S
1							
2							
3							
4							
5							
6							
7							
8+							

MOOD

Week 52 Date

MONDAY

TUESDAY

WEDNESDAY

THURSDAY

FRIDAY

SATURDAY

SUNDAY

"True contentment is not having everything, but in being satisfied with everything you have."

OSCAR WILDE

CONTENTEDNESS

NOW THAT YOU'VE SPENT 52 WEEKS NURTURING YOUR NESS, TAKE SOME TIME AND WRITE BELOW ABOUT WHAT YOU HAVE LEARNED AND HOW BEING MINDFUL HAS CHANGED YOUR LIFE. BE SPECIFIC. HOW WILL YOU CONTINUE TO USE WHAT YOU'VE LEARNED THIS YEAR?

MISCELLAN

EOUSNESS

NOTES • MEMES • PLAN • COLOR • CREATE

WORDINESS

WORDINESS

WORDINESS

WORDINESS

WORDINESS

SOCIALNESS

YOU'VE SURVIVED 100% OF YOUR BAD DAYS

YOUR ATTITUDE DETERMINES YOUR DIRECTION

DON'T LET ANYONE STEAL YOUR JOY

THINK
POSITIVE
TALK
POSITIVE
BE
POSITIVE

A LITTLE
PROGRESS
=
BIG
RESULTS

YES!
YES!
YES!

SUCCESSFULNESS

JOT DOWN YOUR GOALS ON THE LABELS BELOW. CUT THEM OUT AND PLACE IN A BOWL, PULL ONE OUT WHENEVER YOU NEED A NEW CHALLENGE.

Read a book a week

Run a 5K

Bake homemade bread

Goal Bowl

DOODLINESS

DOODLINESS

DOODLINESS

DOODLINESS

COLORFULNESS

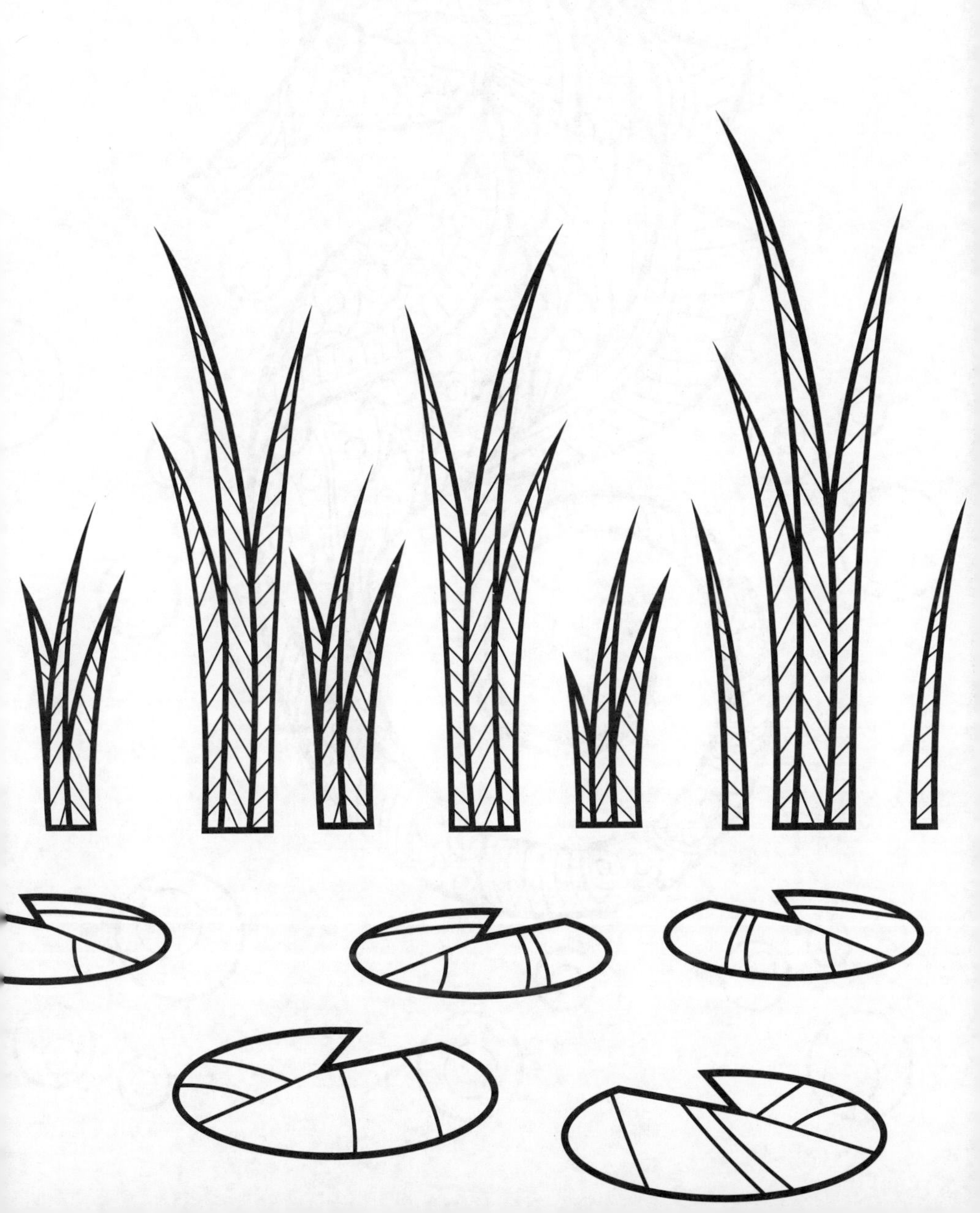

COLORFULNESS

COLORFULNESS

COLORFULNESS

COLORFULNESS

FARSIGHTEDNESS

					1	2	3	4	5	6
7	8	9	10	11	12	13	14	15	16	17
18	19	20	21	22	23	24	25	26	27	28
29	30	31	32	33	34	35	36	37	38	39
40	41	42	43	44	45	46	47	48	49	50
51	52	53	54	55	56	57	58	59	60	61
62	63	64	65	66	67	68	69	70	71	72
73	74	75	76	77	78	79	80	81	82	83
84	85	86	87	88	89	90	91	92	93	94
95	96	97	98	99	100	101	102	103	104	105
106	107	108	109	110	111	112	113	114	115	116
117	118	119	120	121	122	123	124	125	126	127
128	129	130	131	132	133	134	135	136	137	138
139	140	141	142	143	144	145	146	147	148	149
150	151	152	153	154	155	156	157	158	159	160
161	162	163	164	165	166	167	168	169	170	171
172	173	174	175	176	177	178	179	180	181	182

183	184	185	186	187	188	189	190	191	192	193
194	195	196	197	198	199	200	201	202	203	204
205	206	207	208	209	210	211	212	213	214	215
216	217	218	219	220	221	222	223	224	225	226
227	228	229	230	231	232	233	234	235	236	237
238	239	240	241	242	243	244	245	246	247	248
249	250	251	252	253	254	255	256	257	258	259
260	261	262	263	264	265	266	267	268	269	270
271	272	273	274	275	276	277	278	279	280	281
282	283	284	285	286	287	288	289	290	291	292
293	294	295	296	297	298	299	300	301	302	303
304	305	306	307	308	309	310	311	312	313	314
315	316	317	318	319	320	321	322	323	324	325
326	327	328	329	330	331	332	333	334	335	336
337	338	339	340	341	342	343	344	345	346	347
348	349	350	351	352	353	354	355	356	357	358
359	360	361	362	363	364	365				

KEY ☐ ______ ☐ ______
☐ ______ ☐ ______ ☐ ______

INDEBTEDNESS

To Momala, for always being proud of me—even
when I didn't make it easy.
To Paul, for the love and support.
To Lucy, for being the world's cutest writing partner.

NURTURE YOUR NESS
WRITTEN & DESIGNED BY BEN MARGHERITA

Copyedited by Jo Ann Liguori
Mandalas designed by Visnezh
Coloring Illustrations by Kaewtasiri

FIREPLACE PUBLISHING

ISBN: 978-0-578-78076-4

Printed in China
1 2 3 4 5 6 7 8 9 10

SEE YA!

WEBSITE: nurtureyourness.com
FACEBOOK: NurtureYourNess
INSTAGRAM: @nurtureyourness
MEDIA INQUIRIES: nurtureyourness@gmail.com